Miracle Bab[y]

By Janelle Wilson
Illustrated by Artkina Celestin

Miracle Baby

EduExcel LLC
Copyright © 2021 by Janelle Wilson

Contact us at eduexceljw@yahoo.com
ISBN 978-1-7367960-0-9

Design by Artkina Celestin. Text set in Freude and Century Gothic. Artwork was produced in Adobe Fresco and Adobe Illustrator.

Dedication

God, YOU continue to smile upon me, and I sit in awe, amazed by this work and with humility. Thank you, Father for your grace, mercy, love, and for the many miracles that you have performed in my life.

To my wonderful husband, Jason, thank you for your tremendous love and for consistently being my biggest supporter and motivator.

To my three modern day miracles, Malachi, Micah, and Christian, what precious jewels you are. I am BLESSED to be your Mom!

Special thanks to Apostles Eric & Carolyn Warren, my spiritual parents, for your guidance, and for always speaking to my destiny.

To my Equippers City Church Family, thank you for your overwhelming support and steadfast prayers.

To my "Editing" Sisters, your contributions to and throughout this Miracle Baby journey were invaluable!

To my Family and Friends, thank you for encouraging and pushing me to complete this project and for always having my best interest in mind.

To all of my fellow Preemie Parents, thank you! Your little ones are fighters because of your tenacity and determination to see them thrive.

Finally,
To my Mother, Emma, although you have entered unto your heavenly rest, thank you for being there from the very beginning! Because of your prayers, sweet spirit, and sacrificial love, I am the woman that I am today!

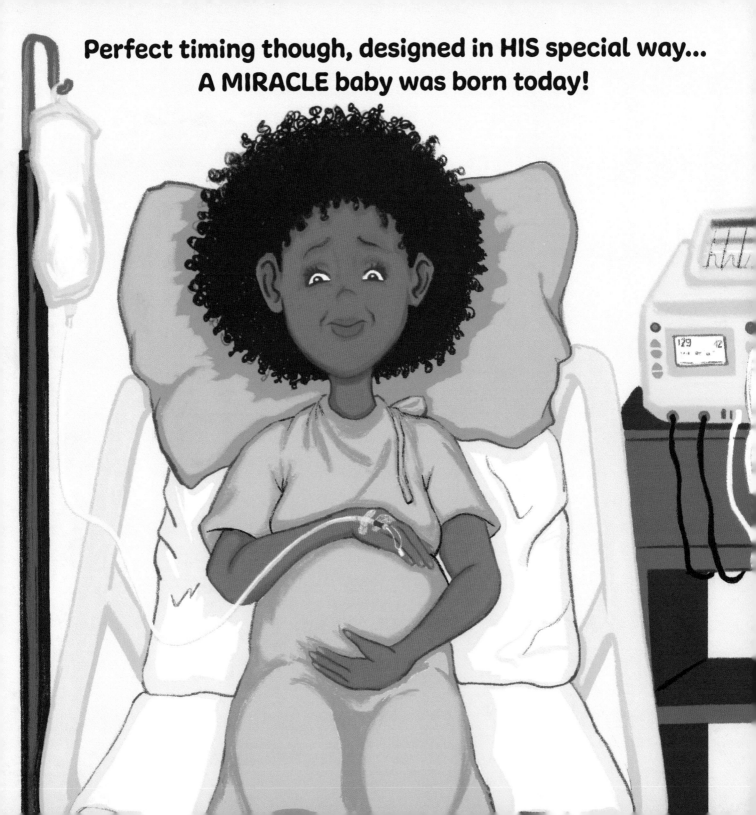

Introduced to the world, yet quite a bit early
So STRONG and POWERFUL,

CALENDAR

March
x x x x x x x
x x x x x x x
x x x x x x x
x x x x x x x
x x x

April
x x x x
x x x x x x x
x x x x x x x
x x x x x x
x x x x x

May
x x
x x x x x x x
x x x x x x x
x x x x x x x
x

June
x x x x x x
x x x x x x x
x x x x x x x
x x x x x x x
x

July
x x x x x x
x x x x x x x
x x x x x x x
x x x x x x x
x x x x

August
x x x
x x x x x x x
x x x x x x x
x x x x x x x
x x x x x x x

September
x x x x x x
x x x x x x x
x (16) 17 18 19 20 21
22 23 24 25 26 27 28
29 30

October
          1 2 3 4 5
6 7 8 9 10 11 12
13 14 15 16 17 18 19
20 21 22 23 24 25 26
27 28 29 30 31

November
                1 2
3 4 5 6 7 8 9
10 11 12 13 14 15 (16) BABY IS DUE!
17 18 19 20 21 22 23
24 25 26 27 28 29 30

so fit for the journey!

A small little package, so fragile, so tiny

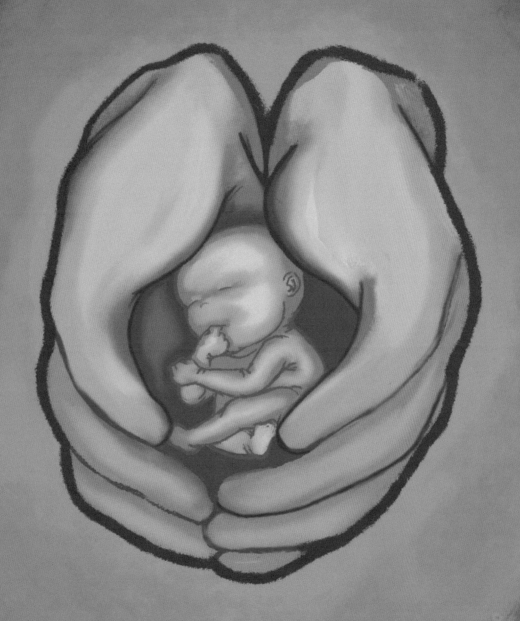

Has great things in store and a purpose so
MIGHTY!

Yes, a lot of things have been added to you

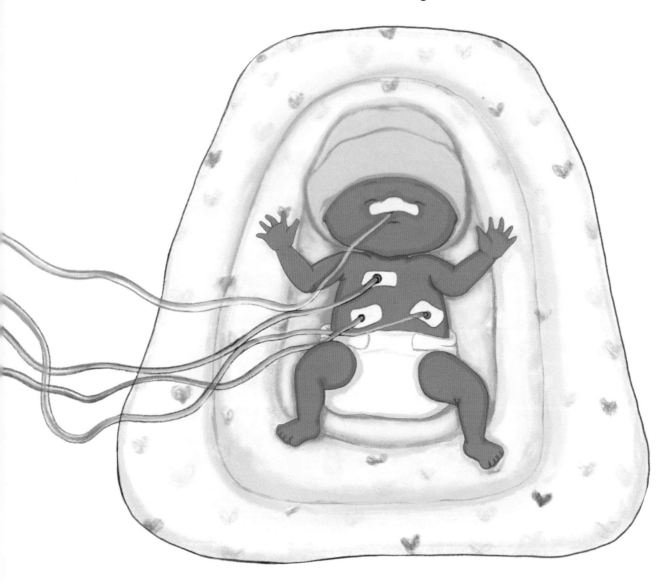

**All for your protection
and safety from boo-boos!**

Tucked gently away in your own little home,

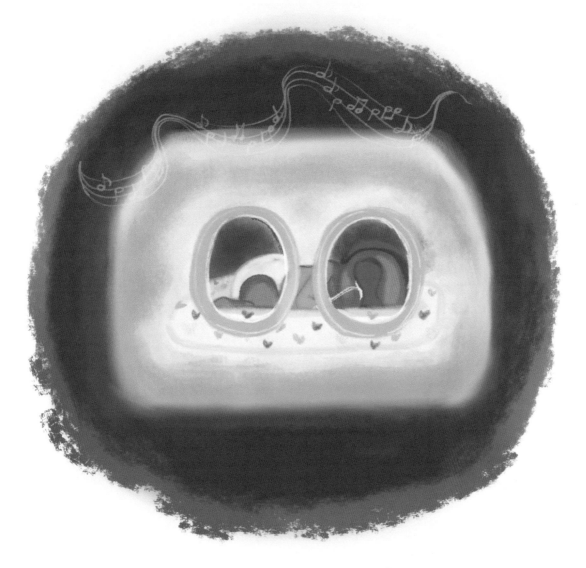

Lights dimmed, soft music, so that our precious can grow!

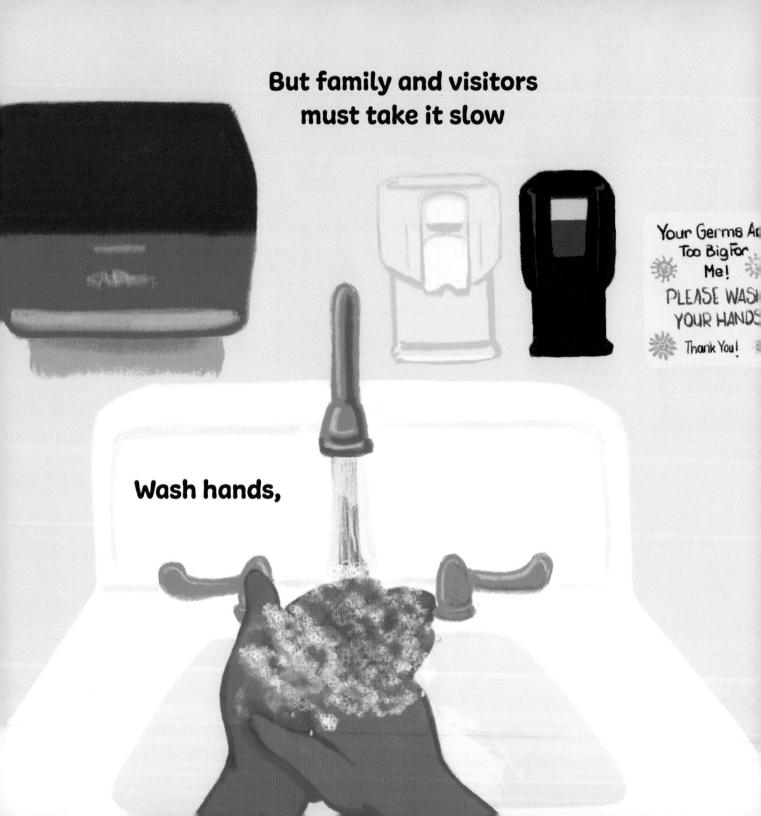

Sign in,

Tip toe in your room,
Please, no loud noises, clashes or BOOMS!

A MIRACLE baby was born today!

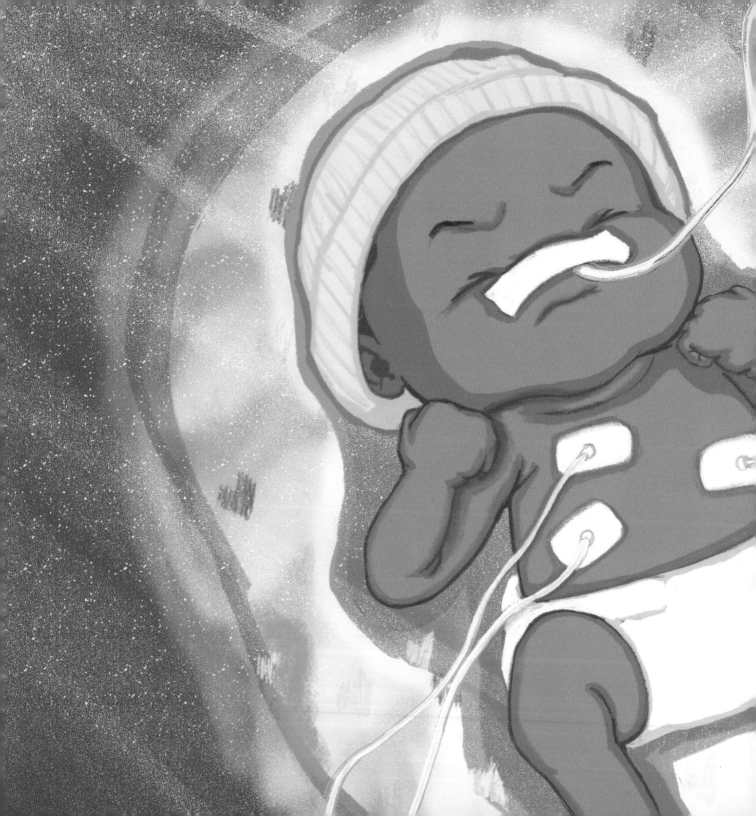

God says,
"For I know the plans I have for your life
Plans for prospering, good health...
You were born to FIGHT!"
It may be a while before you are released
So rest in Him,
He's your perfect peace.

A MIRACLE baby was born today!

First time in clothes

first bottle

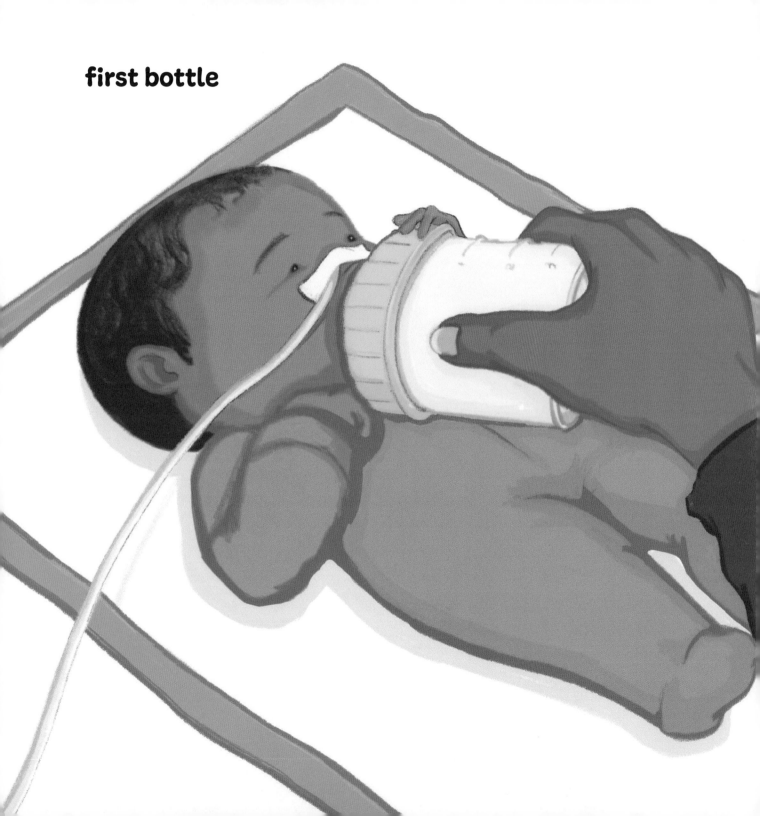

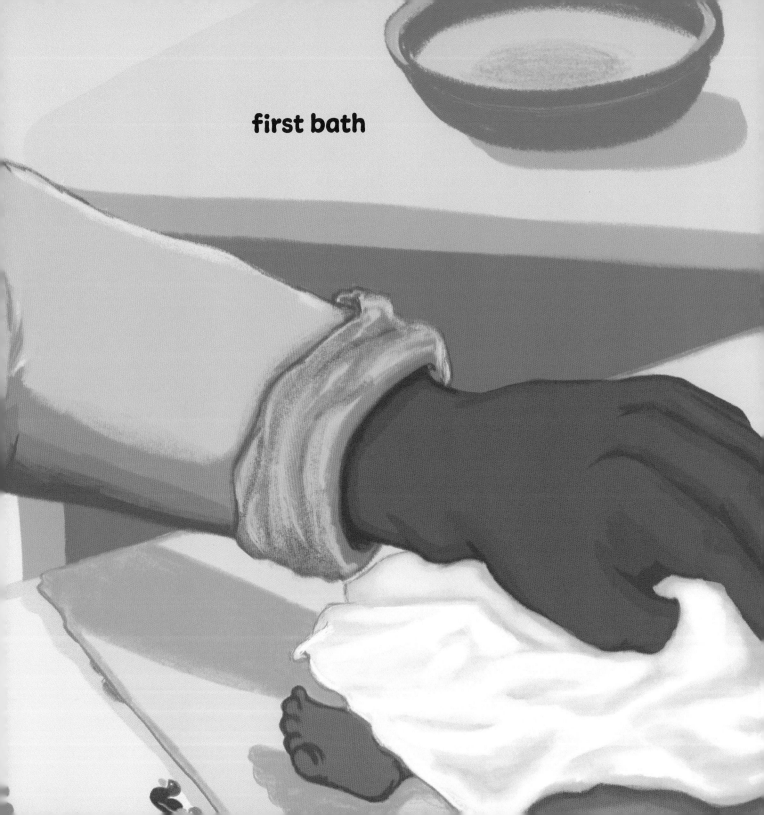

first bath

to you may seem like
a daunting task!

"Be strong, of good courage,"
God would say,
"You're an OVERCOMER!"
He made you this way!

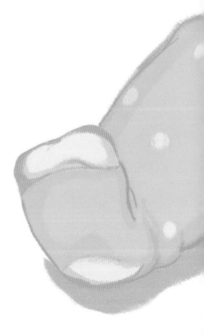

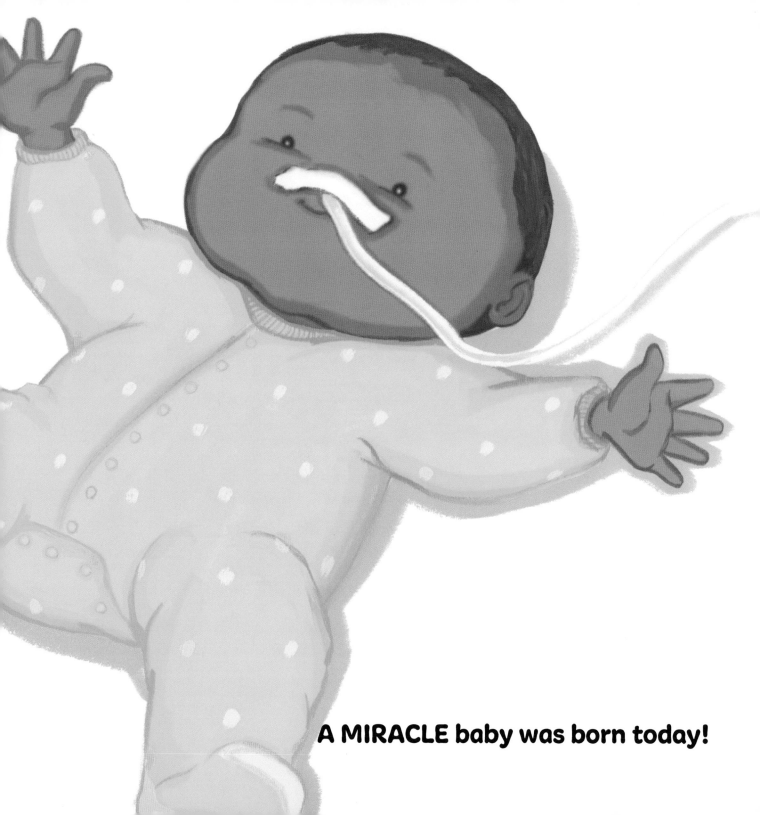

A MIRACLE baby was born today!

Daddy and Mommy are EXCITED you're here
A little nervous, unexpected, with concerns and some fear.

Be ANXIOUS for nothing, give thanks and just pray.
God knows the time I'll be ready to play!

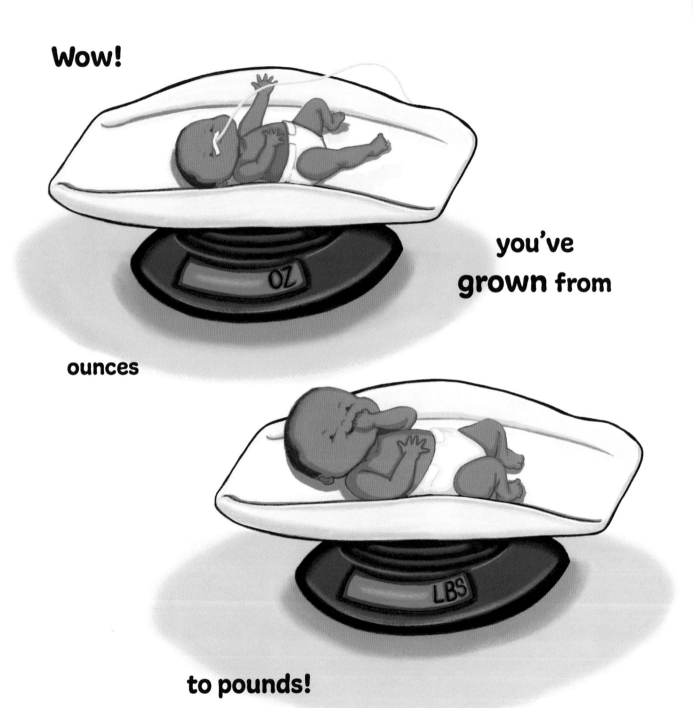

Wow!

you've
grown from

ounces

to pounds!

New expressions on your face,
you're familiar with sounds

Now, you breathe on your own,
No tubes or machines needed

Our prayers are being answered,
not just met---but EXCEEDED!

A MIRACLE baby was born today!

Such a **Wondrous** story behind your birth

Each challenging moment is priceless in worth

Watching you **grOW** more and more each day
We are thankful God gave you to us this way!

Some babies are born much earlier than others

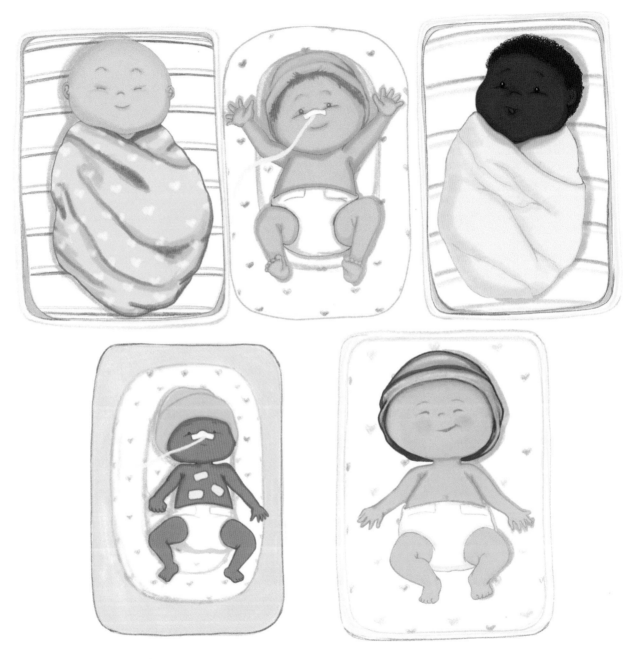

Unique in their size, with a gift to discover!

So little, so sweet, so soon some might say
Perfect timing though, designed God's special way...

So glad our MIRACLE baby was born today!

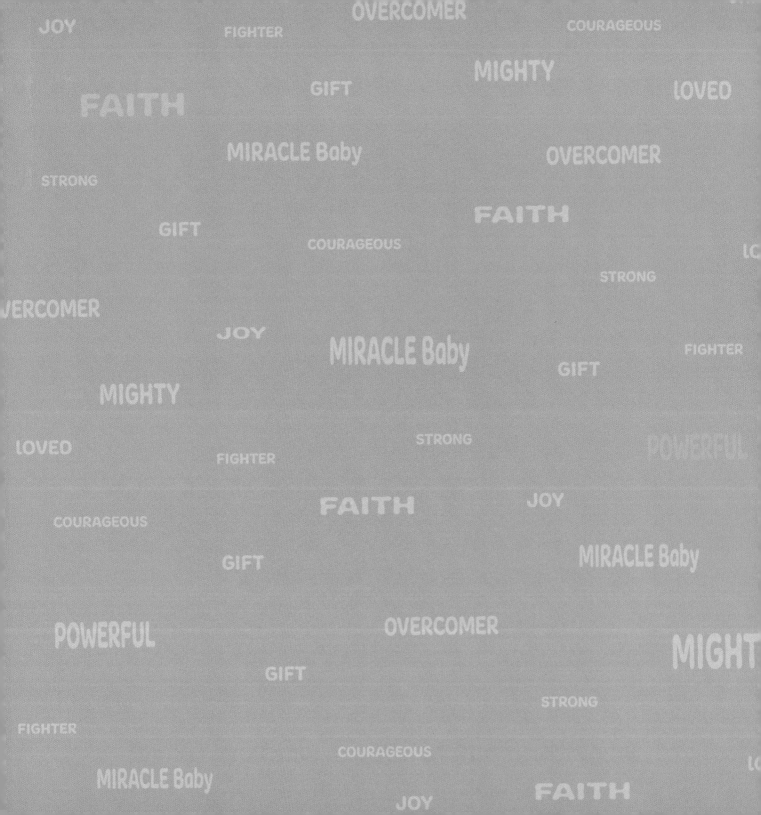

Printed in Great Britain
by Amazon

26604183R10021